what Does it mean to be Brave?

ISBN 978-1-7773574-0-5

To my grandma
who helped me to
find my brave.

to be brave?

Does being brave mean climbing a mountain?

Does being brave mean swimming with sharks?

Does being brave mean singing a song on a stage?

Does being brave mean going to the moon?

Does being brave
mean walking
into a dark cave?

Does being brave

mean jumping from

the highest diving board?

Being brave isn't just big and scary things in far off places.

Being brave happens every day.

Being brave isn't the same for everyone.

Different people need
to be brave for
different things.

About the Author

Kelly Shuto is a kindergarten teacher
on the west coast of British Columbia, Canada.

The inspiration for this book came from
watching children learn to support each other,
to persevere through challenges
and to find their brave in everyday situations.

Kelly is a proud mom of two
adventurous and active boys.

She loves spending time exploring in nature,
laughing with friends
and watching her children grow.

Educational Information

Ideas to Encourage Deep Thinking About Bravery

Have children write and/or illustrate their own page about what bravery is to them.

Using "loose parts" materials, ask children to tell about a time when they were brave.
If they are comfortable and ready, individuals can share their story of bravery.

Each page contains a hidden heart to represent bravery. Ask students to draw, write or explain a symbol that represents bravery to them.

Go through each page one at a time and talk about the meaning behind the words and the illustrations.

Use the discussion questions to help encourage deep thinking and connections to the concept of bravery.

Discussion Questions

When was a time that you were brave?

What connections did you make to this book?

What connections did you make to others
(characters, friends, family members)?

How can you recognize, support and celebrate
bravery in others?

Why does bravery mean different things
to different people?

What is the connection between perseverance and bravery?

What is the connection between confidence and bravery?

What does bravery mean to you?

Why is there a heart on every page? What symbol represents
bravery to you?

When have you noticed bravery in others?

How is bravery represented on the back cover?
Where might we see examples of bravery in nature?

CPSIA information can be obtained
at www.ICGtesting.com
Printed in the USA
BVHW021726260321
603220BV00003B/9